ZAWADI

WRITTEN BY ANN WANGARI
ILLUSTRATED BY ROBINSON OMOL

It was a warm Friday evening and the first week of Zawadi starting a new school. It was the longest, most exhausting yet exciting week she ever had and she was happy to have made many new friends.

Zawadi had to introduce herself to many children and although she was usually confident, she didn't feel confident on this particular week because everything was too new for her. The school was bigger than she had imagined, and the older kids were like giants in her eyes and she also had to adapt to a new way of doing things, compared to her previous school.

Zawadi knew she had lots of talents and she could not wait to show off her talents to her new friends! Unfortunately for her many of the kids in the new school were just as talented as she was, and some were even better than her! For example, in her previous school, Zawadi excelled in running but now she was struggling not to come in last because the kids in her new school were a lot faster than her.

She was always the top of her class in painting, music

and math, and her teachers always made her feel special about her performance. But now, everything was different and she no longer had the same attention that she was used to receiving because the kids in her new school were just as good if not better than her.

Zawadi also began to question the way she saw herself. It seemed like some kids in her new school thought differently than she did, and this caused Zawadi to doubt herself. Her new friend's parents also bought them the musical instruments they wanted and paid for private music lessons.

But Zawadi's parents did not earn enough money to afford the same things for her. As she listened to all these new kids talk about themselves and what they had she began to think less of herself and she started to feel unhappy about her life.

When Zawadi got home she went to her favourite place in the garden which was the swing. Normally she would be joyful and laughing when on the swing but today, her thoughts were on her new school and especially how different her life was compared to her new friends. These thoughts made her really sad and just as she was about to start crying, she began to feel something in her heart. It felt warm and loving and she focused on what was happening in her heart,she realized that she did not need to cry.

"what is this"?

She asked, and as she took a moment to think about what had happened, she remembered the soothing voice of her Nana Esther saying

"Yeshua is in us".

Hmm... could this be Him and is this warmth his love? Nana Esther also said Yeshua was a good friend, always with her and she could ask him any question.

Zawadi whispered hesitantly,

"Yeshua, I am confused, please tell me who I am?"

No sooner had she whispered the question, she felt herself moving faster than she could think. She noticed a dot of light suddenly turn into what could only be described as a living mirror, shimmering as it resembled a swirl of light.

Zawadi was not afraid, in fact she felt so much love, peace and acceptance in a way that she has never experienced before, as she stood before the light. She immediately knew that Yeshua was the doorway to the kingdom of her Father in heaven and because she believed him, there was a knowing in her heart that heaven was home and it was as close as her next breath.

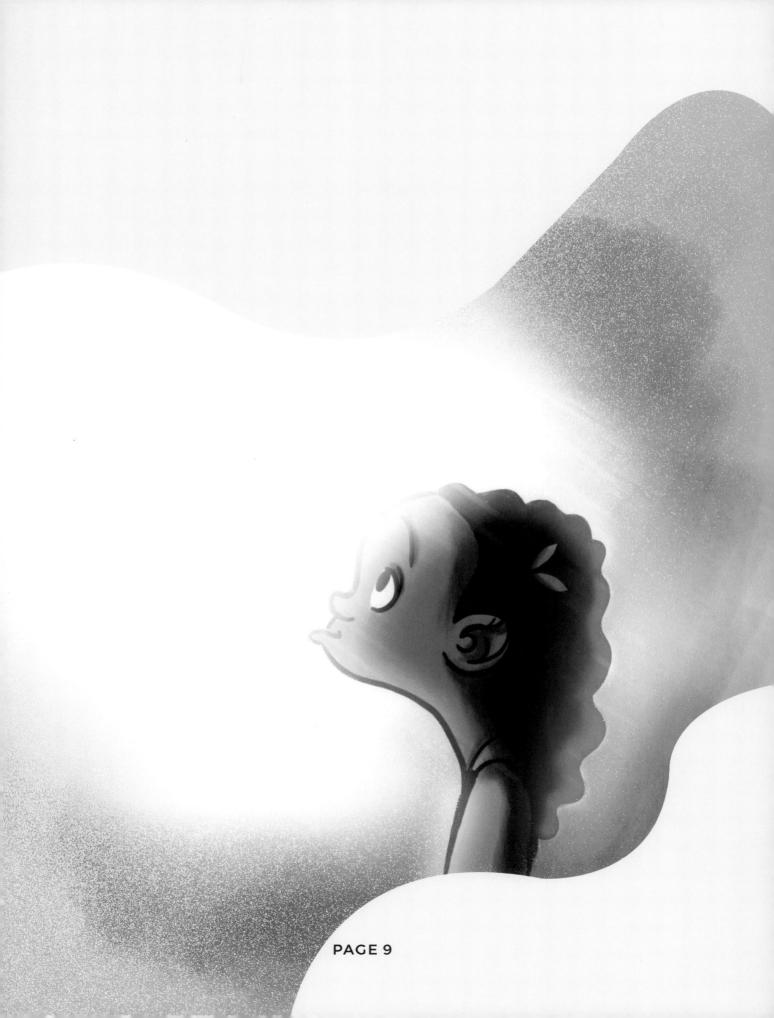

As she approached the living light, she heard the most beautiful song coming from the light. The song was about who she was before the creation of all things. She remembered she was and still is light that was always in God before she was in her mother's tummy.

In that moment, she knew she was never alone. In fact the love of her heavenly father was flowing like a fountain right through her, bringing joy and hope in her beautiful heart.

The floor beneath her looked like a magnificent clear sea and there were many angels of various colours all around her, as well as people from various nations and all ages. But what caught her attention was the most magnificently brilliant light, brighter than all the lights in that place. She could not take her eyes off of the light. It was Yeshua and He was perfect and radiant.

All her fear left as she stood before Him, because he made her feel like He was her best friend. She got the feeling He was all that she needed and this made her feel that everything that had happened that week no longer saddened her.

Instantly, she saw herself through the eyes of Yeshua and began dancing and shouting with much excitement because she now believed what it meant to belong to Christ.

"I don't have to be like the other kids or allow what I am good or not good at to define me. Yeshua loves me and accepts me, and I am thankful for my family, my new school and my new friends. Thank you Yeshua for the talents that you have given me and I know that you will help me get better as I settle in my new school". As soon as she said these words, she knew she was ready for another week at her new school.

Zawadi then opened her eyes and she had the most beautiful smile as Zawadi opened her eyes, she realized she hadn't stopped smiling which then turned into excitement as she couldn't wait to tell her parents what had happened.

ACTIVITY

WORSHIP

You can sing, dance, put some worship music, paint, write or be quiet before him.

Remember that Jesus enjoys your company and rejoices over you with singing.

See yourself stepping inside of Him like you do when you step in your house where you are safe and warm. Remember that He lives in you and in Him, you live, move and have your being. Worship him from that place.

Be free to express how you feel. Even if you feel a bit sad. See yourself laying that sadness under his feet and walk away from it because He is your helper and His blood is powerful to set you free from everything.

WAIT ON HiM

"Wait for the LORD; be strong and take heart and wait for the LORD". Psalm 27:14

Find a comfortable space and silence your mind. Remember that He is with you always. Tell him that you want to feel His presence, see Him and hear His voice. Silently wait for him to come and encounter you. He can come to you whichever way He chooses, just as he has done in the Bible and is still doing so now.

His answer can be a picture in your mind, a physical visitation, a word, a whisper, a dream, you can feel His tangible presence in the room, a bible verse or whichever way He chooses. When He answers you, thank Him and write it down.

Do this everyday and keep a record of your encounters with Him. He is a friend who loves your company and the more you spend time with him the more you get to know Him even more, know His voice and also He gets to change our hearts in those moments.

PRAY

Thank you Father, Holy Spirit and Yeshua for loving me very much. Thank you that you are always with me and I do not have to fear anything.

Thank you that you alone define me and my identity is in you, created for you and for your glory.

My future is written down and I choose to surrender to that future. Open my eyes and ears to see and hear you. Thank you that heaven (Your kingdom) is as near as my next breath and through Jesus, you have provided a door for me to step in heaven at any time because it is my home.

Thank you for (remember what he has done for you like giving you family and friends and thank Him for that).

As I wait for you, teach me how to love you and give me boldness to speak of your love for me and my relationship with you to my friends and family.

ABOUT THE AUTHOR

Born and raised in the beautiful land of Kenya, Ann now lives and works in London. Her passion is to see love and freedom awakened. When she is not writing, she loves to spend her time with family and friends exploring nature, trying new food, having long chats and a good laugh.

ABOUT THE ILLUSTRATOR

Robbie is an extroverted creative, who loves to interact with people and is constantly on the lookout on how he can improve how people see things, whether through his music or through his art in graphic design. He is a believer and his music is geared towards influencing his generation positively through a message of love and truth.

Zawadi

Zawadi series is an invitation for both the
young and the hungry at heart
to journey into the heart of the father and to
have a personal relationship
with the Godhead.

—

To get in contact with the author please
email her at

---

zawadiworld@gmail.com

Contact the Illustrator

info@romol.co.ke

Zawadi
Written by Ann Wangari; illustrated by Robinson Omol

Illustrated by Robinson Omol

Published by Seraph Creative in 2020
United States / United Kingdom / South Africa / Australia
www.seraphcreative.org

ISBN: 978-1-922428-13-4 (print)
ISBN: 978-1-922428-12-7 (eBook)

SeraphCreative
Heaven's Heart for Earth

Seraph Creative is a collective of artists, writers, theologians & illustrators who desire to see the body of Christ grow into full maturity, walking in their inheritance as Sons Of God on the Earth.

Sign up to our newsletter to know about the release of the next book in the series, as well as other exciting releases.

Visit our website :
www.seraphcreative.org